Miracles
The Wonder of Life

by Walt Whitman

ILLUSTRATED BY D. K. STONE

RAND McNALLY & COMPANY

CHICAGO   NEW YORK   SAN FRANCISCO

Why,

who makes much

of a miracle?

As to me

I know of nothing else

but miracles,

Whether I walk the streets
of Manhattan,
Or dart my sight
over the roofs of houses
toward the sky,

Or wade with naked feet
along the beach

just in the edge of the water,

Or stand under trees in the woods,

Or talk by day with any one I love . . .

Or sit at table

at dinner with the rest,

Or look at strangers opposite me
riding in the car,

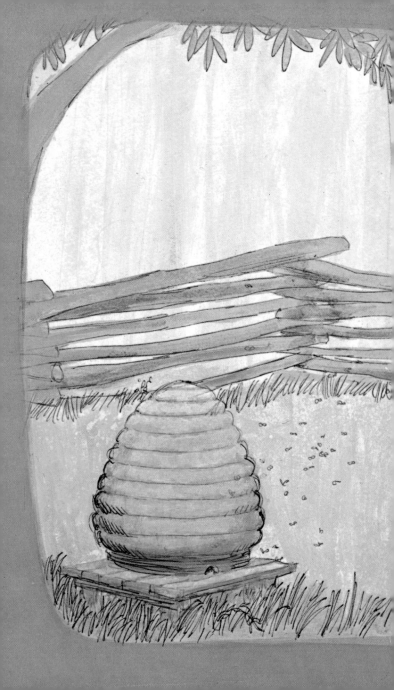

Or watch honey-bees busy

around the hive

of a summer forenoon,

Or animals feeding in the fields,

Or birds,

or the wonderfulness of insects

in the air,

Or the wonderfulness
of the sundown,
or of stars shining
so quiet and bright,

Or the exquisite delicate thin curve

of the new moon

in spring ;

These with the rest,
   one and all,
      are to me miracles,
The whole referring,
   yet each
      distinct
      and in its place.

To me every hour
   of the light and dark
      is a miracle,

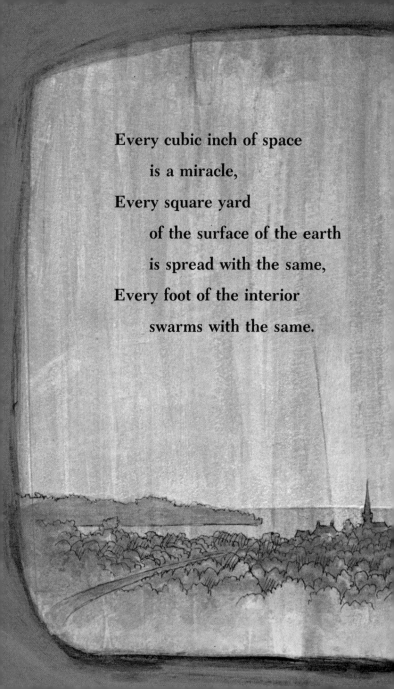

Every cubic inch of space
  is a miracle,
Every square yard
  of the surface of the earth
  is spread with the same,
Every foot of the interior
  swarms with the same.

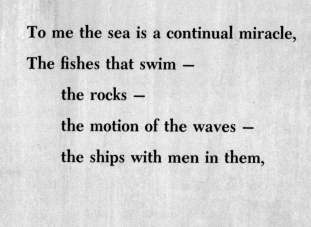

To me the sea is a continual miracle,
The fishes that swim —
    the rocks —
    the motion of the waves —
    the ships with men in them,

What stranger miracles are there ?